WRITERS ON EARTH

WRITERS ON EARTH

New Visions for Our Planet

Edited by
Liza Cochran, Brittany Collins,
and Clare McFadden

Published by:
Write the World LLC
One Mifflin Place
Suite 400
Cambridge, MA 02138
United States

www.writetheworld.com is the global platform for student writing.

Editors: Liza Cochran, Brittany Collins, and Clare McFadden
Cover Design by Inkahoots
Illustrations by: Emma Barry and Liberty Mountain
Book design and production by: Happenstance Type-O-Rama

ISBN: 978-0-9975867-2-5 (print book)
ISBN: 978-0-9975867-3-2 (ebook)
Printed in the United States of America

Table of Contents

PART II: POEMS

PART III: NARRATIVE

Foreword

"WHAT TO MAKE of a diminished thing?" Robert Frost's oven bird famously asks.

The young authors in this volume pose variations on this essential question.

How to survive in a changing climate?

How to find beauty in a degraded world?

How to value a nature that is slipping away?

"The earth was made to hold life—to nurture it and cherish it . . . we are bringing about change so quickly that earth can no longer cope with it," observes Jyotsna from India.

"Earth is resilient, humans are too, but not as," Grace from the US writes.

"I'm going to try and love all the pieces that never should have come together, mostly because I have no other choice," Shanti from New Zealand says.

I found their poems and essays to be haunting—wise and honest and true. I think you will, too. Even in the face of environmental destruction, these young writers manage to find inspiration in a "diminished thing." This collection balances their sense of fear with their sense of wonder.

—Elizabeth Kolbert

Introduction

YOUNG PEOPLE HAVE, throughout history, been catalysts for transformative societal change, but have never before confronted an existential predicament that affects the world's population as broadly as climate change. It is the young people of today, Gen Z, who are showing all of us how to face climate change head on. It is young people who are leading and guiding us—galvanizing adults into taking action.

In the pages of this book, *Writers on Earth,* a global problem is reduced to its purest form: "Saving Ourselves from Ourselves" reads the title of one piece; "Sound the Silent Alarm" reads another.

The act of bringing the world, in all its complexity, into singular focus is as bold as it is necessary. Today's youth are growing up in a world that faces a far more consequential environmental threat than any that has come before it. As critics dismiss their demands as naïve or unrealistic, an entire generation is gathering its collective voice to say, "We have no choice," or, in the words of Greta Thunberg, "Our house is on fire."

Through this collection of reflections, essays, stories, and poems, this generation bares its heart. From the disappearing maya birds in the Philippines, to the invasive stoats and possums in New Zealand, to finding oneself stranded on a park bench amid a raging flood, these writers share their thoughts, fears, and hopes about the global environment, its future, and our place in it. The world of climate change is their world. This generation knows no other.

Yet even in the face of environmental destruction and fear, these young writers find beauty all around them. This collection balances nature as a force of destruction and worry with its power to transport and transform. From Canada geese nesting amid urban detritus, to wild bougainvilleas eclipsing an abandoned house in Old Delhi, to star searching beyond the cityscape of Abu Dhabi, to the wonders of a backyard berry patch—this collection portrays the precious fragility of the natural world's rhythms in these turbulent times.

Writers on Earth offers a new take on a longstanding genre. Many of these Gen Z writers grew up in the world's busiest urban centers. Rather than equating nature with the pristine and pre-served, the pieces collected here represent the environment as all-encompassing: the toxic dust in Bangkok, the rain in Manila, the skyline of Kerala's capital. The collection is forward-leaning in its capturing of nature within the urban setting, while also looking backward at a disappearing landscape through the borrowed eyes of the authors' parents and grandparents, from Singapore to Canada, Australia to Pakistan, the US to Japan. Reading these pages gives the opportunity to hear young people speaking to each other about their lives and their futures.

These pages are more than a stand-alone anthology. Rather, they extend the vibrant community of young writers found at Write the World (*www.writetheworld.com*)—the global online gathering place for 13- to 19-year-old writers. Instead of reck-oning with the weight of today's issues in isolation, these writers share their words with one another *in real time* as they publish, read, and peer review one another's work. Speaking across geographic, cultural, political, and social divides, they set an example for all of us through their unwavering dedication—both to their cause and to one another. They are reason to hope.

These young writers speak across generations as witnesses to an accelerating world. *Writers on Earth* captures this pivotal moment for perpetuity. May these words continue to crisscross the globe—spirited and insightful, cautionary and bold—reminding us to pay attention.

—*The Editors*

Editors' Note

The young authors of the following poems, prose, and essays were all high school students at the time of writing their respective works. To find out more about these young writers, please take a look at their biographies at the end of this publication. Our Reader's Guide can also be found at the back of the book—it contains questions and suggested activities to prompt further thinking and creative work in response to this anthology.

EMMA BARRY

Part I

REFLECTIONS

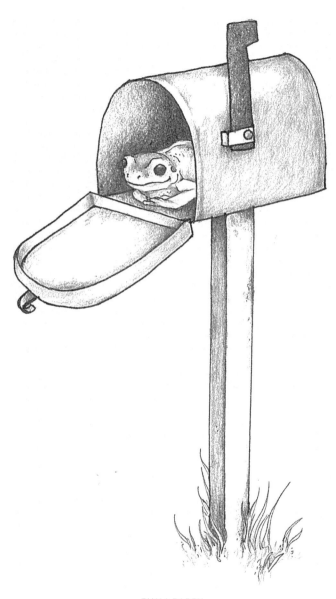

EMMA BARRY

Peepers

Emily Rice, 16

UNITED STATES

MY DAD CALLS late Sunday night and tells us to come and hear the frogs, so my brother and I hop in the car and drive to his warehouse in industrial West Eugene. My dad joins us, and we make our way down the street toward the rusty yellow gate that leads into the wetlands. We pass by a row of mailboxes—when we were little, my brother and I used to run up and down this street checking every mailbox for tree frogs. They like to make homes there, and it was like Christmas finding a frog in the mailbox. We would scoop them up and cup them in our hands and examine the stripes on their backs with wonder, then set them free and watch them hop away through the tall, muddy grass.

Back then, the wetlands across from my dad's shop were lined with native willow, alder, birch, and towering cottonwood, and the graffiti-covered wooden lookout on the edge of the marsh used to sit tucked in a dense grove of trees. Tonight the three of us stand in the lookout that now stands alone, a stark silhouette against the endless marsh grass, and the soda cans at our feet reflect a rainbow of city lights.

On a normal night, traffic and industrial clamor drown out the night music of crickets and honking Canada geese. But tonight, a full moon in March, a chorus of croaking drowns out the industrial din, and the geese and crickets and everything, even my own voice. The three of us peer from behind the wooden, graffiti-covered wall, looking out over the pond where a flock of Canada geese sleep, nestled beside the reflection of the full moon, and my dad raises his voice above the croaking to tell my brother and me about the spring peepers that used to sing their way through the silent night when he was a boy.

Dynamics, Predators, Islands

Shanti Mathias, 18

NEW ZEALAND

THE WORLD KEEPS CHANGING. It changes when I don't want it to. It changes, and the temperature rises. It changes, and an undiscovered species goes extinct.

I am afraid of this change.

I know the world as it is, the trees I walk around, the birds that call. I cannot imagine it as it isn't: dry and desolate, or lush and forested, like it was before humans walked the land.

There are traps through the New Zealand wilderness, traps to kill ferrets and stoats and weasels and possums and rats. All were introduced by various settlers to this country.

And they devour. How they devour. They place their teeth around birds' nests, native birds that have never known that they're prey. They crack the eggs and consume the contents.

No more new kea and kakapo and takahe. Dwindling populations. Loss. The ever-present shadow of extinction. A climb up the list: threatened to endangered to critically endangered.

My aunt tells me of the people she knows, lovers of the environment, who bludgeon the possums until their bodies are stilled.

The possums are eating the bush, the birds, the world. They are being possums. They are surviving in the environment they've been introduced to. They are pretty: wide eyes, slinky tail, soft, dense fur.

Their lives are placed below those of pukeko and tui and piwak-awaka. They eat millions of tonnes of the forest that was here first. They are unwelcome immigrants: loathed, vilified. They are doing what possums do.

The world has changed, and humans are (mostly) at fault. They bring greedy animals to pristine shores. The ecosystem will never be the same, even if the kea population recovers, if the predator free islands protect the kiwi.

Is it ridiculous to continue to save these creatures, the original inhabitants edged out by the voracious newcomers? It can't be. I treasure memories of heavy kereru gazing at me from their hiding place in a bush; the black robin, hopping closer, curious, cheerful.

Is it unfair to vilify these creatures who have found themselves in a new environment and survived so well? Yes. The weasel is lithe; it flows like water. It is beautiful. It is not evil. It is the way it's made to be: hungry, just like the birds.

I don't know how to reconcile these two: the birds, beautiful and essential and absolutely part of the world they belong to, and the animals that kill them, because they know no other way.

Really, it's the humans who are at fault, the humans who are always agents of change and death and renewal. We know no other way.

The environment is changing. Species are going extinct. One day, we'll be one of them; we'll dissolve like carbon in the ocean. But for now, we have to accept dynamism and accept the breaths that ascertain our own life.

Love the ferrets and the kaka. Treasure the deer and the tuatara. It might be best if they exist in separate spheres, but the world has changed now. I'm going to try and love all the pieces that never should have come together, mostly because I have no other choice.

For Florida

Sophia Bloom, 17

UNITED STATES

IN FLORIDA, the effects of a changing environment are visible all around us. Lakes are often left desolate and cloudy as a result of a process called hypoxia, where chemicals cause algae to infest the water, resulting in an ultimate depletion of oxygen. Duplexes and condominiums tower where forests once stood only a decade ago. The weather grows ever more unpredictable.

This is especially distressing to me, because this is where I grew up. This is where I spent my childhood. Children of the future may never experience my memories of combing the shores of Sanibel Island for seashells, or of hiking through pine-and-palmetto forests to see a red-tailed hawk swoop overhead, or of learning about the wonders of the marvelous mangrove trees. In the future, Sanibel may be underwater, the pine-and-palmetto forests may be replaced with those of concrete, and the mangrove trees may be declared extinct. In the future, my memories of Florida may be reduced to just that—memories.

I don't care about climate change because of politics, and I don't care about the environment because people say I should. I care because this is where I live. I care because of the mighty alligators, the sawgrass forests, and the cry of a whip-poor-will after dark. I care because of my friends and family, and their descendants, and those who come after them.

I care because this is Florida, and this is my home.

Into the World

Lei Mesina, 13

JAPAN

WHEN I FIRST touched snow, it was midnight in the middle of nowhere.

The ride there was probably what I liked second best. It was hours away from home, but the first time I saw snow was from the car. It was late afternoon on the same day, and the very moment we emerged from the tunnel, the snow hit the windshield. I was the only child in the car, and three grown-ups turned their heads to me at the same time. Mom nudged me and said, "Well? It's snow."

I remember she whispered afterward, "Pretend to be excited."

But the spot itself was gorgeous. I forgot about the racoon we almost hit on the way.

There was a lamppost illuminating the thick bed of snow so that it shone blue. There was a bench, too, caked in snow. The memory is blurry, but I remember every single speck of snow descending upon my face as I made my first snow angel. And my second, third, fourth . . .

My parents were in the car, but that was after Mom took a picture of me.

I was alone then, but I didn't think much of loneliness, because when dreams come true for a child, their world is complete for a time. My world right there could have been compressed into a snow globe. My footprints in the snow, a lamppost, my parents' car, and a bench.

Maybe I imagined the bench. The memory is blurry.

The difference is quite distinct from the times when I made "snow" out of shredded tissues and baby powder. I didn't need an electric fan for the snow to rise and trickle down the air.

The snow was on my eyelashes, and I took off my beanie.

There was a strange happiness in solitude that I didn't notice until that moment. I didn't notice how Time stopped. I forgot about sunrise; and dangerous rides down slippery highways; and the family of deer that could have been staring at me through the trees. And selfishness didn't exist because I had everything. I forgot about myself, too.

And then Time ticks again. And the color fades through time, and another artwork is seen.

Now, a few years later, I wonder.

I wonder why I now yearn for someone to share the small space of my snow globe with.

EMMA BARRY

LIBERTY MOUNTAIN

Where Have They Gone?

Rain Castañeda, 17

PHILIPPINES

SEEING THEM FLY across the blue sky makes me think of the crisp, brown autumn leaves dabbed with the first drops of snow. A few times in a week, this bird called maya would sweep down on our graveled yard and feed on the fruits of the aratiles tree. My father used to be irritated when these birds from the family of sparrows would defecate on our lot. It's because their feces looked like a puree of the aratiles fruit, which would later harden on the windshield of our car.

Regardless of what they did to my father's poor automobile, maya birds were good companions. My parents never attempted to shoo them away when they would chirp on our veranda. They taught us to never hurt even the smallest of living things. My mother would say *may pakiramdam din sila,* meaning *they can feel too.*

I used to pet these birds when they would relax under a nearby tree, and I'd feed them with fruits and seeds. But this memory was from ten years ago, and I'm starting to wonder where they are now amidst these high-rise buildings.

One time, amidst the monotonous routine of life, my classmates found a frail bird outside the school entrance. Its brown and white feathers struck me—it was a dear old friend, maya, taking its last breath.

I felt sorrow seeing the bird, after a long time, moribund and helpless. The maya is known as an urban bird, but as my fingertips stroked its feathers, I worried that modernization had grown so assertive that even these resilient creatures were feeling harassed.

As I looked into its tiny eyes, I felt a yearning for a lost friend, a memory that flew away with time.

This Quiet Northern Wild

Astrian Horsburgh, 19

UNITED STATES

MAYBE YOU WOULD CALL it the bias of blood, my mother's ancestors calling me back, but the northern reaches of Norway have fastened a deep hold on me. I have been there so rarely that the north coasts and the distant Lofoten islands have attained a mythical lure in my mind—were the sunsets really so carefully crafted, a watercolor fugue above silhouetted peaks? Were the small red fishing cottages, rorbuer, really so trim and crimson, perched pert and unassuming on the shoals near the racks where fish dried under the crystal northern sun? The memories are starkly visual, a softly blurred silent film. My limited Norwegian is a shoddy skeleton key to the lilting dialects steadfast against southern Norwegian's standardization—I can speak in my halting second-generation lexicon, and the words will fit into their ears, but I cannot decode theirs in return.

Not speaking was better—who needed words? The language I understood was the communion with the sky, the mountains, jagged facades giving way to sloping green hills cradling a cove of white sand. On the beaches, I picked shards of ocean-battered plastic out of the sand, the refuse of other times and places deposited by the ceaseless waves on this place I could not therefore call pristine.

Breathing was easier here, the air not infected with haste and angst. Pausing for the maturation of a thought or the passage of a feeling was possible in a way I have not found in any place marked by urbanization, industry, any of those trammels of "modern civilization."

I stood on a dock in Reine, blinking back tears at the sensation of standing among human dwellings not heavy with hubris, the touch of humble hands that did not assert a greater scale or importance than the land that abided them; I ate a thick fish soup on a cliffside restaurant deck while the sun gilded the rooftops of Henningsvær and we lost our words to describe it; I climbed down a hillside to the drowsy hamlet of Nusfjord, whose silence spoke of composed, time-polished solitude, its resting heartbeat low but its pulse steady—a far cry from the dying towns and hollowed-out neighborhoods that scar the US rural landscape. This was not a realm of ghost towns, except perhaps the ghosts of Western civilization's smothered cousin, what we could have been had we not chosen to bruise and gouge the land instead of honor it, if we had understood that no monstrosity of metal and human cunning and suffering would ever send spirits soaring higher than the crisp quiet grace of land that knows both how to speak and to listen amid this troubled world of clamor and deafening static and shattered peace.

LIBERTY MOUNTAIN

LIBERTY MOUNTAIN

One for the Basket, One for Me

Tessy Waugh, 14

CANADA

I FEEL MY arm slap instinctively at the mosquitoes crawling up my thigh. I wave them away, but occasionally the lucky blood-sucker gets her needle-like beak into my flesh, and I feel a sharp sting. The hat I'm wearing does little to protect me against the sun, and I can feel its warmth on my forehead, drawing out beads of sweat just as bubbles appear in a pot of boiling water. Clammy and sticky, my hands pick raspberries from their thorny homes as fast as they can go. Sticky, warm juice trickles across my palm, and when I smile, the dried juice in the corners of my mouth cracks and sticks.

Tartness! Oh, how my mouth puckers up! My taste buds tingle, and my cheeks hollow! Followed by sweetness, so deep and strong and luxurious. I let it roll over my tongue, I bask in it. The seeds are occasionally gritty, and my mouth and teeth feel like a mortar and pestle, respectively. Somehow there is no way to describe the taste, but with the word "red." It's rich, and yummy, and underestimated! It's full and sweet, and something beautiful and tangy! The juice bursts from the skin, and explodes in my mouth.

It is so loud, yet so quiet all at once. A dweller of busy cities would find the silence deafeningly conspicuous, yet the trained ear could hear all the levels in the cacophony. Distant braying of sheep, rustling of raspberry leaves . . . the odd strained whinny of a horse. I hear all these things, each an intricate lacy layer of sound. Wind breezing by my ears, trees bending towards their neighbours, and cars speeding along bendy roads. Bees lazily buzz between blooms, and sheepdogs arc towards their flocks, herding them in neat rows. Then there is the constant swish, everlasting and soothing, of my quest heading for the berries.

The Forest . . .
No, Stadium, in My Backyard

Jyotsna Nair, 15

INDIA

WHEN I WAS SIX YEARS OLD, I would sit on my mother's lap in the back seat of the car. My perch allowed me to see many things—the chaiwalla smoking cigarettes at his shack, movie posters plastered on brick walls, and the forest that bordered our colony.

Forest was the perfect word for it—too large for woods, too close to human habitat for jungle, yet too wild for park. All I knew about it was that it perfected the sunset; from our terrace, you could see the last rays of light crown the tops of the coconut trees before fading away into twilight.

When I was nine, two announcements were made. One: we'd be moving to England for a year. This news was delivered by Mom. Two: An international stadium would be built where the forest now stood. The state government informed us of that. I was too young to realize that the latter was the more important issue. On the way to the airport, I saw cranes and JCBs at work, uprooting trees and large lumps of chalky white rock.

I returned home a year and a half later. I had grown three inches; the stadium had swelled into a massive concrete behemoth.

On the way home, I saw large floodlights and paved paths. All that was left was a coat of paint, and then it would be inaugurated. I attended the august function, along with a dozen neighbors. The ribbon was cut, and the name revealed: Greenfield International Stadium.

Stadium was okay. Even International I could cope with, although it was a bit of a hyperbole. But Greenfield? No way. The stadium stood on the graves of trees; on the decayed remains of shrubs and weeds and the homes of birds. Greenfield was the least apt name they could've picked for a structure that quickly made us feel the heat in the summer. *How could they?* I thought. It was wrong.

I never realized what we've been doing to the Earth until I experienced it, just a few yards away from my backyard. The Earth was made to hold life—to nurture it and cherish it and eventually become its grave. And we are destroying life—trees, animals, and even our fellow human beings. We are bringing about change so quickly that the Earth can no longer cope with it. It's rebelling—each increase in the carbon dioxide levels, each melting ice cap, each smog cloud, is a warning. Or, rather, a plea to stop. Recently, Kerala suffered horrific floods—my relatives were trapped in their homes for a week. The Philippines was wrecked by a typhoon. Earth isn't localizing its pleas. The more we destroy, the more urgent they become—until we listen.

The world I live in is one of change. A tiny change in the atmosphere of a newly born, fizzling lump of rock (known today as Earth) that billions of years ago evolved oxygen, making life possible. But change is also why we're hurtling into a global catastrophe—or, more precisely, climate change is why we're hurtling into a global catastrophe. We have to change for the better now, to save our world.

Drought

Olivia Campos, 15

UNITED STATES

I DIDN'T KNOW water could run out. Water was omnipresent—dripping from the faucets, gushing from my shower head, going stale in a bottle in my backpack. It wasn't even a consideration in my nine-year-old mind until the drought warning was issued.

It doesn't rain in Southern California. On the odd occasion that it rains for a few hours, or at most a day, streets flood, businesses close, roads are redirected, simply because our cities aren't built for it. But when I realized we had gone all winter without having to take a different route to school, I knew something was wrong.

Seven-minute showers were heavily encouraged. You couldn't water your lawn unless it was after six. Water bills went up. Public pools were drained. All small things were said to make a big difference. Clouds were light and transparent, never carrying rain or any sort of weight. Those that did simply blocked the sun; they never stayed for long and often hurried away to rain on some other fortunate place.

It killed me that the biggest body of water on the planet was ten blocks away, and we couldn't use any of it.

The drought warnings went away a few months ago, but the effects remain. Lawns that hadn't been converted to water-saving desertscapes are still brown and lifeless. Low-flushing toilets are almost a standard in restaurants. The pools were never refilled and have now become makeshift skate parks for kids who are too young to remember anything different. But life continues, gratefulness fades, and we have all gone back to driving under our palm trees and complaining at the occasional twelve-minute storm.

But at least now, when I turn on the faucet, I know that the water comes from somewhere.

Part II

POEMS

Seagull

Mai McGaw, 17

UNITED STATES

Some days I feel
Like a lone seagull
Gray and white creamy feathers and yellow beak,
Circling, feet tucked up to its chest,
Between the glaring window eyeholes of mundane office buildings,
So far from the sea.
So far from the blue and the spray and the wind,
Trapped, prisoner of the air currents that carry it
Wings outstretched
Around and around,
Like ripples in water, above our dirty city streets
Observer and witness to crimes committed against ourselves
And of carelessness and the numb wandering of our people who
        have no leader
To cry, "Rise up, rise up!"
And if the gull should cry, to scream out our sins, would anyone
        listen?
To us, in the streets down below, the gull holds so little
        significance.
A prophet that only I recognize, looking upward
Like prayer in a church, and wishing I could see
The gull's eyes and what in them it held,
For our homes of brick and pavement and disappointment:
Love or hate or cool indifference?

Wishing, I could be borne away
On the gull's soft feathered back
To a place of spray and wind and water
To be pulled back to the sea with the comings and goings of
    the tides
To be immortalized forever,
Cremated and excused from the heavy burden
Of humanity and citizenry,
To float on the waves, a message bottle
Stuffed overfull of intentions and memories,
And dreams to be held eternally still and perfect and never
    to fade,
Made smooth by the sea and sand like pieces of sharp glass
The edges so rounded that they cannot cut my fingertips when
    I pick them up,
In my mind, some days
I am the seagull that has been thrown
Cruelly far above the high tide line of sticks and stones and fine
    sea foam
Circling above a fortress of resources and power
Misused
Drifting on currents of wind that shift between the buildings
    like sand
All wishing, all begging
To return to the sea.

In My City

Vani Dadoo, 16

INDIA

In my city
If you lie on the roof
of a sixty-something skyscraper to stargaze
you'd have the proof
from the stars, stray and ablaze
that you are still as insignificant.

In my city
If you drive on the bridge over the sea
that separates cities and mountains
you'd see
and wonder at the waves, whelming and wanton,
and not at the beams that hold up the bridge.

In my city
If you walk along and look at the coast
from your house of wood and metal and brick
you'd want to boast
that the water tries to worship and lick
your feet and your hands and your soul.

In my city
If you notice the electric tower rising in the skies
across the highway, the lonely street

you'd recognize
an emerald creeper climbing, not discreet,
unaware of electricity, but thriving on it.

In my city
If you stand on the beach and see the sun drowning in the sea
and behind you there is a row of commercial buildings
you'd agree
that the dying, red sunlight seems to be gilding
the glass windows and the metal girders.

Untamed Beauty

Eva Terry, 14

UNITED KINGDOM

When the rushing of the world enters my head,
slipping through my ears and eyes and fingertips,
And it whispers to me "look at this and this and this
And this and this andthisandthisandthisandthis"
Until it is a blurred hiss of necessity,
I seek the sky.
Its reflection on the wide-open sea,
Which with its chaos can create and destroy.
Where the tides of the moon can mingle with the rushing
And drown it out.
I seek the dappled sky, peeking between rustling leaves,
where whispers aren't pushing and probing, but warming.
The perpetual sounds of life.
I seek the feeling of the wide-open sky baring itself to me,
Honest and real,
Over a field of long grass,
Softly caressing my legs, reminding me
I am Here.
Among all this wild beauty,
like the untamed magic of a wild fairy,
With hair falling like momentum,
And eyes bright and daring.

I am Alive,
And I am Myself,
Me.

Give Me Back My Winter

Gen Ryan, 15
AUSTRALIA

I miss your gloved hands,
This Winter, I miss your hugs,
I despise the heat.

In June

Ainsley Kennedy, 15

UNITED STATES

Green carpet spread out beneath the sunshine,
swaying in the breeze—
the scent of cut grass lingering as blades flop defeated
on the hot asphalt

crossing the driveway without shoes, feet still wet
from the garden hose, listening to
birds chittering at the empty feeder

Sky overhead is blue-blue-blue like a robin's egg,
commandeered by cumulus clouds towering above

there is the smell of hostas blooming,
and the sharp scent of tomato, too;
my stomach rumbles, and I sneak a raspberry
from the patch in the backyard, savoring
its tart sweetness while it lasts

Chiloé

Elisa Troncoso-Cabello, 13
UNITED STATES

i watch the horses

and they're staying where the grass grows higher
and the weeds reach up to their flanks
but we can get close enough to reach out
and touch one, where the hair bristles on the edge of its spine

the ground is patchy and dark
but who
could look at the ground
when all you can see are the dark ocean waves
and all you can hear
are the seals crying from the rocky islands

i can smell the salt and the earth
and the wind would blow me away
if i were not so grounded
grounded in this moment

but when i climb el muelle de las almas
and i scream out for the ferryman
to carry me into the sky
i can only hear the wind answering back
and horses run

LIBERTY MOUNTAIN

Metaphoric Trees

Aliyah Banerjee, 13

UNITED STATES

They're green chandeliers on oakwood doors.
They are the musical clocks of the seasons.
When they are felled, they rise yet again.
Home to chirping music of the dawn.
And listless spirits by night.
Dewy leaves crying tears of farewell.
Whispered secrets on windy days.

Never Forget

Akhila Bandlora, 16

UNITED STATES

i.

The girl with sea foam fingers writes letters
on napkins left on beaches like loose change,
words stumbling down staircases of five-seven-five haikus
—*i want an ocean,*
the one mama whispers of,
when she eats, sleeps, prays—
she ties them to the webbed foot of a seagull,
sends it off to the governor—
"the tide is coming."
he laughs, the kind of laugh that corrodes,
shoos the seagull—lulls it to sleep with plastic wrappers and bottles—
throws the napkin away to land exactly where the girl found it,
dips his pen into the seagull's carcass to sign a bill
for a factory to dump their industrial waste into the ocean
—man made trashcan.

The girl's eyes are seismic; the world shifts.

ii.
It's 1972,
the year oysters pearl, fish jump, and crabs claw;
the girl trades her haikus for ballads, her flat chest

for fruit cup breasts, their apathy for her unrest
the sailors; they call her a woman.
she gargles the sea in her mouth to remember why she's fighting,
pulls trash left on beaches and from washed up animal carnage,
dumps it on the governor's desk—
"the tide is here."
chants reduce, reuse, and recycle outside the homes of
	oil-guzzling men,
she leaks into classrooms, salt water ferments the walls,
teaches her children how to protect;
the world watches her,
until its eyes cataract,
teeth chip,
lips parch,
and ears burst.
And finally, it listens—
births the *Marine Mammal Protection Act*,
MPRSA, the *ocean dumping act*,
holds the UN Convention on the *law of the sea*—
All promises to defend.
she smiles,
whistles to the whoosh of the waves,
and shows her children how to protest—
The fight is not over.

iii.
It's 2017,
where climate change is an alternative fact,
the ocean an afterthought instead of a forethought;
but it's still her first thought.
her bones are soft like coral,
hair long like coast and gray like gravel,

voice throaty as a frog's—
her battle ending,
the war still raging—
her children, we do not forget;
when our president pulls out of the Paris Agreement,
elects a denialist to run the EPA,
cuts its budget by thirty percent,
we grab conch shells and march on—
"the ocean is rising and so are we"—
she braids kelp through her hair,
washes her body with the sea,
tells us to never forget,
and we say we never will.

Anthropocene Echoes

Shanti Mathias, 18

NEW ZEALAND

Most of us know we'll leave something behind.
Most of us want it.
On my most selfish days, which are most of my days, that is what
    I want.
Leave an impact. Change the world. These are easy things to
say, and how they're said, in valedictorian speeches and inspiring
tweets and in heartfelt father-daughter advice.
I do want to change the world.
But I don't want to remember that I have already changed it.
I don't want to remember that hills become holes so I can type
on a silver laptop I'm proud to own. I don't want to remember
the devastating storms that wrench Pacific islands apart as I fly
over to continue my education. I don't want to remember that
my leather bag was made from the skin of animals whose sweaty
bodies rubbed far too close together.

There's ruination coming. Some people have received it already. I
have not. Maybe I
never will.
Unless I choose.
I can choose to share pain and alleviate suffering. Somehow.
Somewhere. (These are clichés of their own. I'm not going to
stop being allergic to them).

I will make wrong choices. When my days are measured, I'm not sure if the net balance will be positive or negative. But for today, I'm choosing to have hope.

I live in the Anthropocene. The world is never going to be the same. I'm not sure I want to change it . . . but the change has happened, and it's not going to stop. I'm going to use every shred of courage I can find to admit that again, and again, and again, and then try to make up for it.

Winter Sunrise

Kasey Delben, 16

AUSTRALIA

When the rush of chill wind lifts your hair
and runs icy fingers gently down your spine,
when your breath makes a fine cloud in front of you
and your fingertips are hidden warm and safe in the depths of
    your jacket,
when the first sight of the sun makes your breath catch
as it dances along the lines of your face,
lighting the spark in your eyes like the glow of a fire
and dipping the distant tree tops in a golden layer of light,
when the horizon stretches out in front of you
like a blank page waiting for the first touch of ink,
when the birds trill, but quietly,
as if hesitant to mar the hushed glory
of a newborn day
not yet christened by the touch of the sun's rays,
when your heart feels ready to burst free
of its small cage within your chest,
do you feel alive?

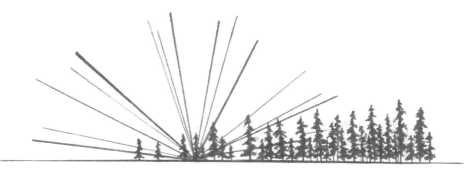

LIBERTY MOUNTAIN

Creeper in a Crack

Vani Dadoo, 16
INDIA

There was an abandoned house
in the mazes of Old Delhi
at the end of a narrow street
it was known for being an ancient suite
(for the nobles)

The conquest was started by the birds
who settled in on the terrace
mated, birthed, built their nests
comforted by the lack of guests
(they were many, years ago)

Then, there were creepers in the cracks
dandelions in the brass hinges;
wild bougainvilleas leaped over the walls
over the years, till the neighbor falls
(and still complains)

The plant in their courtyard
was nurtured into a tree
by the birds, the mice and the rats and cats
who spread the water, built grass mats
(now the house houses a tree)

The wood is in a war
with the brick and the paint
branches have broken the windows
leaves dance with the wind and shadows
(an ugly mess of bark and glass)

Will it stand, will it fall?
The paint is gone, the house is torn
roots have broken the tiles
the moss has taken to the wall, a victory vile
(it has become an untamed garden)

EMMA BARRY

LIBERTY MOUNTAIN

In September

Gayatri Rajan, 14

UNITED STATES

She turned knobs all evening.

Still the binoculars remained
unfocused on the scaly spines of leaves,
the bluebirds' spiky feathers, the crimson wild
of a blooming autumn.

Open maps of brilliant orange
wallpapered the earth.

This is how revolutions start,
she thought, focusing her full attention—
a fistful of fire, a scrap of birdsong.
This is how worlds change. Imagine,

a single dawn melody whispering daylight
in the earth. Entire cities rising
from a breath of autumn smolder.

She aimed at the highest treetops,
caught a plane settling,
witnessed leaf's spiral, pendulum-flash

of brown. Aimed the eyepiece
again: slip of wing, silver
of moth, curl of sunset. Autumn sharpening.

We Ran as if to Meet the Moon*

Nida Mir, 15

PAKISTAN

A gilded sceptre for the King of the sky
An ornament for a starry shawl
A starry shawl for the women in nature
And a portal from heaven to earth
An enlarged star just for you
A porous orb made just out of Noor

A stringed pearl in an angel's wing
A wolf's howl
And a wanderer's lamp
A white spot on an inked page
A calm sight after a stormy rage

A marbled gem on a veiled face
A poet's pride and a writer's gaze
Periwinkle petals in a frosted globe
A luna's crown
Zeus' bolt

A lavender-soaked cotton knot
Of a celestial variety
A lonely thought, a lost memory
A curer of anxiety

*THE TITLE OF THIS POEM IS BORROWED FROM ROBERT FROST.

Thoughts from a November Morning

Kate Gardner, 15

UNITED STATES

Have you ever thought about
how you are aware of your limbs
of where they are in space
even when you can't see them

I rest my hands on the bark of a dying
maple, his body insect-hollowed
I hope my warmth lingers, a comfort,
as I try to plug up the holes in his body

beneath bark and lichen both
(if I disregard the interlopers)
he is smooth

I have a secret, I am fallible,
an animal still, I hope no one sees as I
heavy my breath, a huff and a puff
as I try to cloud the street with vapor

simply for the strangeness of the sight
steam engine, I am,
am I?

a woolly bear caterpillar in my way
brown stripe black stripe brown
again, I pick him up just to run
my fingers down his spines, feel his

little cupping feet, they cup not enough
he falls from my grasp

Heartbeats

Mai McGaw, 17

UNITED STATES

On a frosty October morning, I walk to a field
   And lie flat on my back in the dewy grass,
You can hear,
If you listen—
     The birds, singing
You can smell,
On the breeze: woodsmoke
Beneath this soil
     There is something
Moving like the blood rushing through me
   Pumping
     I know
There is water here, flowing downhill
      Flowing,
If
     I close my eyes,
      I can see the rivers,
Blue veins on a wrinkled hand
      Lying here
In the dewy grass,
    The raindrops, splashing across my face and
      When I turn on the faucet in my mind
   I am reciting a sermon
     In my mind,

I am giving thanks
        For water that flows,
            Wet and clear
   I do not forget the memory,
     Not my own, but someone else's, captured in black ink
Of sand, pouring
        Until it filled the kitchen sink and spilled over
       Onto the tiled floor
      I do not forget the memory—not my own
But someone else's
       Captured in the pages of a book
Of dry ground,
    And no well for thousands of miles
      I do not forget the memory, not my own
    But someone else's
       Of water that blazed
Into burning
Brilliance   when struck
     With
A single match,
        I do not forget the memory,
    Not my own, but someone else's
Captured in scribbled letters
      Of water that betrayed,
   Water that brought illness
         not strength
I give thanks
     For the water that flows clear and cool
   Just enough and not too much
      I give thanks for the water
That flows down from mountain springs
       And tumbles from ever-gray skies

To land in the palm of my hand,
      Here in this city,
    We have struck clear blue gold: here we are all kings
         Collecting treasure in the empty bowl on the back porch
            When I was a child, I used to pretend
That the drops on my cheeks were tears
      It made me feel somehow
   Bigger
A part of the mother
          Beneath my feet, my back, as I lie in the grasses
The land that bleeds this water
       Into our shaking, cupped palms
      Until we milk her dry
    leaving her with a dusty husk
And broken promises
       I give thanks for the water.

EMMA BARRY

The Cardinal

Lindsey Maurer, 13
UNITED STATES

Every morning my friend visits me,
A small bird, perched upon a blossoming branch,
Not scared, but casually watching.

She sits on her branch and stares at me,
Brown, unassuming feathers lending themselves
To the small crest atop her head.

Then, like clockwork, she flutters away,
Wings whirling in a peaceful flight, heading home,
Leaving me with just my coffee.

LIBERTY MOUNTAIN

Kingfisher

Pramit Das, 14

INDIA

With his body of ocean scales and throat of burning fire
Listening to the creaking of crickets
In his forest hearth

Kingfisher
His head moves fast
Like a ticking clock
Looking into white-water streams

Whoosh!

He alights his branch
The leaves now rustling
Wings now whirring
Heading towards water with sharpened sight and sharper beak

Splash!

The kingfisher has his meal

Ariel's Gallery

Benjamin Chipman, 17

UNITED STATES

In search of masterpieces,
I descend.

Drifting, submersed in glittering sapphire,
Nature's jewels sparkle—
Illuminated by the piercing sun.
Bubbles ascending to the surface that shields the well-kept secret
Crack at the surface, threatening to expose the treasure below.
But I?
I have the chance to explore
The chance to discover the masterfully curated galleries
Assembled by Mother Nature herself,
And freckled with life
An unparalleled oceanic city of biodiversity.

But that was long ago.
That was in my youth.
The naiveté of optimism,
The naiveté of trust
The naiveté of faith
In those so eager to declare promises,
But so passive, failing to act.

In search of masterpieces,
I descend.

Drifting, submersed in a cloudy diamond,
There was no sparkle, shine or glimmer.
Scattered across the seafloor, once immense colonies
Lay crippled and clinging to life.
Screams of polyps sang toward the waves,
Only to be smothered by the surf.
A seemingly snow-covered graveyard
Lay hauntingly, waiting to be seen again.
Waiting for somebody to notice the tragedy,
A death entirely capable of being avoided,
The loss of a city who entrusted another to its care.

This is now.
This is 2018.
The genocide of Earth's coral reefs,
A bleached, brittle undersea forest decorated with straws and
    grocery bags.
An undersea oasis, now just a memory.
The glory sinks into the past,
And settles into the sandy bottom, never to be discovered again.

In search of masterpieces,
I remember.

EMMA BARRY

Unafraid

Norah Brady, 14

UNITED STATES

Why is darkness surprising,
the ice and the brambles and the quiet,
wild way the wind whistles after dark?

The sky is not a monster under the bed,
only the gentle silk of morning,
and the charcoal of night.

Our fears are our own creation,
the river will roar and crash and kill,
but that is how it is,
and always has been,
blood is not spilt, it is spent and
our hands can neither tame nor object
to nature.

Only look, only touch, only know.

For, in recent memory,
the sun has risen every day
and set every night.
The mountains will remain,
and the wildflowers will find a way,
despite staggering odds,
to grow.

Part III

NARRATIVE

Stranded

Mico Aldmar Tuiza Mendoza, 18
PHILIPPINES

THE CRASH of the unrelenting storm almost drowns every sound—the loud barks of our Shih Tzus in the garage, the cautionary announcements and occasional static on the radio, the loud thumps of footsteps across the whole house—but the whispers of my breath against the window pane grow louder every passing second. For a moment, my breathing falls into a familiar rhythm, bringing me back to last night.

***

It was all the sound I had to distract myself as the loud storm got more isolating.

Slow breath in. Slow breath out.

I was lying on a metal bench in complete darkness, my dirty laundry carefully piled together to protect me from the growing cold. It had been almost two hours since I decided to get off the bus at the entrance hall of a nearby school, after the bus conductor announced that they were going to be rerouting. Apparently, the road through my hometown was declared unpassable. Neck-high flood. The Camiling River had overflowed again.

It was already past midnight, and I was coming home from Manila with all my college work and dirty laundry for the week.

I read from a text message earlier that signal number 2 was raised in the whole province of Tarlac and so I brought my umbrella with me in anticipation of an unusually wet evening. But I did not expect I would find myself stranded alone on a cold metal bench in complete darkness, with only my breathing and the crash of the rain to keep my mind company.

It was impossible to sleep. A multitude of possibilities—ranging from getting killed by a night vigilante to swimming desperately through a flash flood—ran through my mind. My phone had died hours ago, and I didn't know what time it was.

No one knew where I was. No one knew whether I was even safe or not. The absence of time—the absence of certainty—was paralyzing.

This sense of powerlessness intermittently gave me surges of panic through the night—my life and my fate seemed to be no longer up to my own volition, and I could only wait in the darkness for the night to unfold. And for the first time, I understood what it felt like to be trapped—to be stranded. Not just in the physical sense, for beyond being alone and trapped in a dark hall while a huge storm raged on, I felt even more stranded in my own terrifying sense of helplessness in the moment.

***

The roar of thunder breaks me out of my trance, and I'm back to the fogged window pane in our living room, peering out across the cemented patio and onto the drowning yard where brown water silently forms an ocean. The empty lot beside our house is already submerged in flood water, the young banana trees almost drowning entirely, some bottles and plastic floating aimlessly. Even the dirt road in front, extending up to the main road, is now an expanse of brown water.

We're still safe, my sister reminds us every 30 minutes to ease our nerves. Our house has a six-foot elevation from the ground, and floodwater reaching even the first step of our patio stairs is highly unlikely. But my growing fear is not for myself anymore.

As I look restlessly outside the window at the water menacingly gaining volume, images of the people in lower areas flash in my mind. Early this morning, hundreds of online posts crying for help and prayers flooded social media. Photos of districts nearest the Camiling River show they are already swallowed by flood water, flash floods gushing through broken dikes, entire living rooms already submerged, and people—wives, children, babies—trying to survive and get help.

While I worry if the floodwater is even going to reach our house's doorstep, other people are already swimming desperately to survive, climbing to their roofs for temporary safety, crouching and huddling together, praying for miracles. While I sit behind a window pane, relying on the safety and privilege of my home, somebody out there could be all alone on a metal bench in the middle of the dark, stranded. Trapped. Helpless.

I can only hope the storm lets up soon, and that the horrors of Typhoon Ondoy or Yolanda—millions of people displaced and thousands killed—do not repeat themselves. Tropical storms have become more deadly in recent years—and researchers saying warmer sea surface temperatures intensify tropical storm wind speeds and strengthen precipitation have warned us enough to get used to such horrors.

In the days to come, relief operations and rehabilitation will take place. But these short-term compensations can no longer hide the reality that we are in.

The horrors will repeat themselves again: people will shudder in fear again, people will drown and die again, and the wake of tragedy will be another reminder, another regret, another wave of prayers, and another hope for new beginnings. But the cycle never ends, and those privileged enough to survive and privileged enough to be mere observers in this deadly cycle seem to be comfortable enough, safe enough in their own positions. And people who are fundamentally trapped in this never-ending cycle of powerlessness could only remain stranded.

Systemic and policy changes that focus on climate change mitigation and on long-term effects that could potentially mitigate this deadly cycle and save lives are what we need. But a lot of people have yet to grasp that.

A lot of people have yet to experience what it feels to be stranded in a state of powerlessness—to have our fate and our survival outside of our own volition—to realize the immensity of the decisions we make and the cruciality of the change that calls upon us. A change that literally means safety for somebody else. A change that means freedom for somebody else.

A change that means life for somebody else.

Saving Ourselves from Ourselves

Grace Fitzpatrick, 17

UNITED STATES

LIVING IN THE SEASONAL CLIMATE of Massachusetts, I became accustomed to extreme weather patterns during my childhood. This was as most things are—a blessing and a curse; on the one hand, I can confidently say surviving in −10 degree Fahrenheit weather is possible and that 80 degrees is the blessing of a cool summer's day, but on the other hand, I can affirm seasonal affective disorder (SAD) is one of the closest ways a human can get to experience the hibernation cycle of a bear. Still, the area just half-an-hour drive from Boston, where I grew up, relinquishes any trace of city or even suburban life. Forests and rolling hills and farms lie adjacent to the winding Charles. Chameleon green for a time, the palette of a Charlie Brown Thanksgiving Special next, and then for the finale—a milky, crystalized blanket stacked inches (or feet) high.

When in 9th grade, I discovered my mom was offered a job in California, I willingly encouraged her to take it and move us all to the West Coast. And move us she did; Santa Barbara was an intense change of scenery, beautiful in wholly different ways. I loved it, and SAD vanished! The first year here was remarkable.

After school, new friends and I swam and surfed, enjoying driving up and down the 30-something-mile span of surf spots, keeping an eye out for the best wave. Once, I went out on a friend's boat to wakeboard, and we ran into some lovely whales—on Earth Day, nonetheless. It is truly a magical place. To my dismay, all precious things come with a cost; the trade-off for living in SoCal is having to take military showers because of the extreme drought. I could live.

The winter of my second year in California, I experienced, for the first time, a forest fire. The Thomas Fire started in Ventura, not so far away from our little SB cove, and spread rapidly due to the Santa Ana winds. The mountains caught flame and the palms did too. Everyone I know evacuated the area and school was cancelled indefinitely for it was not safe to breathe the high levels of particulate matter in the air; my family left and didn't come home for three weeks. People's pools were used for firefighter water, and firefighters were flown in from all across the country to help. It was a big deal, and it was scary, especially leaving so quickly. How fast a paradise can be destroyed is still unimaginable to me. The fire, however, veered away just in time and few homes within my small city were actually burned. Cautioned by doctors, we had to install air purifiers in our rooms after that.

It didn't take long before our community was hit again. At around 4 am on a January night, a rainstorm instigated a mudslide that catapulted a massive stream of mud and boulders straight through our neighborhood, uprooting homes and killing families. This was the scariest thing I have ever experienced. The night before, our local news station cautioned an evacuation, not a mandatory evacuation, but we still left for the night because we are cautious people. In the morning, we woke to the news broadcasting what looked like our drive home, except there was no freeway, just mud, no little village road, just mud. Cars acted in ways objects act in Dali paintings—so distorted that you could no longer claim the thing functioned how it ought to. After a fire especially, but in California in general, the earth cannot hold the water from a large rainstorm. Plants here do not require much water, and therefore when it does rain, water isn't sucked up by plants. Literally, the water has nowhere to go; the drainage system in Santa Barbara is all but nonexistent because of how mountainous the region is. In addition, the drainage we do have is insanely impractical for rains: when the containment of runoff overflows, it is simply dumped into the Pacific. Because the runoff is not put through the filtration system, pollution from streets, fertilizers, and pesticides is dumped into the ocean, causing numerous issues. After the mudslides, we could no longer swim or surf in the muck-filled Pacific and, to this day, many Montecito houses remain deserted.

It was my surroundings that ignited my desire to find answers—to find out how and why nature works the way it does. I wanted to know what part people played in it. This year, I took AP Environmental Science, a class with the very premise to spotlight how interconnected the world is. I learned: weather is not climate. Even if a senator holds up a snowball in the Senate as proof that Earth isn't experiencing climate change, just know one thing: he's wrong. The climate change we need to look out for is the warming of Earth by 2 degrees Celsius; if Earth's temperature rises more than that, we have little chance of saving ourselves.

I am hopeful for the future because we already have the technology to save Earth and do what we must. The only factor that will change from the past to the future is that my generation, Gen Z, will be the decision makers. We are fully aware of global politics before we are even able to vote, thanks to social media. But with so many outlets and resources consumed by just one individual, filtering to get to the issues that matter is important. In terms of issues we are expecting to take on, global environmental justice is at the forefront of Gen Zers minds, with Greta Thunberg leading the way. I trust my peers more than any adult in decision making because the way we were raised forces us to approach life objectively, without prejudice or precedent in the way. In this way, we are unbound from many chains older generations were forced to operate under—we can work efficiently, collaboratively, and effectively. The only way to tackle a problem as huge as climate change is to hear and value as many perspectives as possible, because there will be that many more solutions and strategies.

Perhaps the most important truth in this day and age is that we need Earth, but she doesn't need us. Earth has survived meteors, several mass extinctions, and two ice ages—how bad would it really be if humans got booted? Earth is resilient; humans are too, but not as. I understand I must do something with what I've learned, and quickly, because time is running out.

Roots

Kimberley Pang, 17
SINGAPORE

IN THE HEART of my grandparents' HDB block, neighbours around the area grew a garden. Not the ones rich with rare species and never-before-seen flowers, but more like a plot of land with shrubs, fruit trees, and some ferns nestled around here and there, but still, undeniably, a garden. Having grown up with it, I guess you could say that my roots were intertwined with those of the plants. But out of all of them, the one that I felt the most connected to was the mango tree that my grandfather and I planted together, right smack in the middle of the humble garden. It was short, unimpressive, but hopeful. It was what connected both of us, a branch from my heart to his.

As I grew older, the mango tree grew taller, and I watched its arms slowly spread over its shorter friends as the years went by. Even though I very much enjoyed watching my green comrades grow together with me, it would be a lie to say I loved the garden for solely that reason. At first, the garden was just a place for me to play with the neighbours' children, but after we outgrew the phase of running around and sweating for fun, they stopped coming down, and I went to the garden for the pure joy of watching my grandfather and his neighbours bond over something that made them happy. It became evident to me that every leaf on each plant was a symbol of my grandfather and his neighbours' hard work and passion, and that made me appreciate the garden's growth even more.

On days the sun scorched, I would watch my grandfather and the neighbours water their plants meticulously, beads of sweat trickling from their hair into the soil, and when it poured, I peeked out the window of my grandparents' 14th floor flat and watched the rain beat against the leaves of our mango tree. I remember how impressively green the garden looked after every downpour. I started appreciating the sun for heating up the ground to just the right temperature for the plants to grow, and the clouds, for quenching their thirst when they needed it the most.

My secondary school days, however, threw my life into what felt like a thunderstorm. The drastic change in workload and life-style took a toll on me in ways primary school had not, and I was held back from a lot of my simple pleasures—including visiting my grandparents and the garden. When I finally took the time out to properly visit the garden, four years had flown by, and I noticed the plants were ever so slightly browning around the edges. It turned out that the consistently above-average temperatures and lack of rain in 2018 made it the eighth warmest year on record, and this, in turn, took a toll on the plants. Apart from that, the familiar faces that met me on a daily basis when I was younger were nowhere to be seen, and it hit me that the plants were starting to wither with their owners.

With the lack of proper balance in temperature and rain supply, as well as regular love and watering from their owners, the plants were slowly but surely losing their brilliant green radiance and were instead wilting into the soil from where they once sprouted. As I watched the years catch up with my grandfather and sickness get the better of him, I realised that the days were numbered for our mango tree as well. Without my grandfather's love and nature's support, it was practically hanging by its last thread-like branch. I tried my best to salvage our tree, but with the merciless sun and Mother Nature's stinginess with rain, it continued to grow weaker by the day, and alas, just like its friends, our mango tree withered together with my grandfather. The curtains were drawn on what once was a humble but beautiful garden, overflowing with heart and soul, a land of precious memories.

Clearing up what was left of the garden was painful yet reflective. I started to wonder if maybe our plants would have survived if nature was a little kinder, if the climate stayed how it was so many years ago. We could've kept the memories of our relatives alive, each fruit the plant bore would have given comfort to so many, as if showing that their loved one would always be there, growing aside them. I know I would've loved to have a memory of my grandfather kept alive, but it was a possibility that could not be explored, and that stirred up my feelings. However, as I pulled the last of our tree's roots, I found a mango—brilliantly yellow, unfazed by the catastrophe that had occurred around it. When I picked it up, I was reminded of how the garden filled the hearts of so many, and a sense of hope overwhelmed me. I thought, perhaps a day would come when the climate would be a little kinder, and the flowers could bloom and fruit trees blossom, and we could all feel the same way I felt when I picked up that last mango.

EMMA BARRY

Sound the Silent Alarm

Sirin Jitklongsub, 17

THAILAND

I WAS NINE when my parents moved all our belongings to the second floor of our house, stocked our bathrooms with black basins of clean water, and filled our bedrooms with instant noodles. It was 2011, and I barely knew how Facebook worked, so I merely watched as my parents scrolled through pictures of people perched on their roofs as torrents of tea-colored water rushed past beneath their feet. I turned on the television and saw boats where there shouldn't be boats, on streets and in buildings and in rice fields . . . or, what used to be rice fields. I thought it was funny at the time, and secretly hoped the floods would reach my area as well, so I wouldn't have to go to school. Living in Bangkok, removed from the struggles of people living in less developed, more affected parts of Thailand, I didn't feel that the floods were anything more than a surprising break from my routine. I didn't know that beneath the boats were bodies, and not just bodies but lost lives, lost dreams, lost futures. I didn't know that the floods were a message from our planet.

Like I said, I was nine.

I was thirteen when the black basins made a comeback in our bathrooms and we started a collection of bottled water. My sister and I weren't allowed to shower for longer than seven minutes each, which seemed like a very short time to me. It seemed ironic, really: we had too much water before, and now we didn't have enough. I was old enough to know, then, that Earth was not just randomly acting out, sending us problem after problem. She had pulled the fire alarm, and not enough people were rushing to save her.

I am sixteen now, and two months ago, I looked out my window and saw fog. Except it wasn't fog. It was dust. Dust like no one had ever seen before. Dust that made global headlines, dust that allowed students all over Bangkok to stay home from school, dust that cleaned out every store's supply of air purifiers. I kept my dust mask on every second I was outside, and yet I didn't stop sneezing for weeks. Then the dust moved up to the northern parts of Thailand and we stopped caring as much.

I took a five-minute walk from my mother's workplace to the train station the other day, and it was blazingly hot.

Interestingly enough, that's what it took for me to realize just how much our world needs our help. Living in Thailand, people are always complaining about the heat, whether they're an office employee or a street vendor (or a student, like me). But how much more complaining will it take to realize that, like the natural disasters that had such an impact on our lives, this heat is more than a passing annual event? How long before we realize that we do not need to look to grand gestures from the planet to recognize the state of crisis it is in? The irregular seasons, the heat waves, the melting glaciers—all are more than natural phenomena: they are warning signs, alarm bells, beeps on the monitor of a planet on life support.

William Shakespeare said: "One touch of nature makes the whole world kin". This is especially true of natural disasters. Like an inattentive partner in a relationship, we force our Earth to resort to desperate measures before we are willing to take notice of the state it is in. Because, when a natural disaster befalls us, for one devastating moment, we are kin. We are family, children of the Earth, working together to save her and ourselves. And when that moment is over, we go back to ignoring her again . . . but we never do stop caring for ourselves. Unfortunately, caring for ourselves usually means exploiting and damaging our blue-and-green home with little to no regard for the consequences. We forget that our planet may survive without us, but we cannot survive without our planet. It's all well and good to take action in the face of natural disaster, but how many of them must happen in order for us to fully realize the growing urgency of our situation? How many of them can we endure before it's too late?

I stepped outside today and there was no flood, no drought, no dust. And yet I knew that our planet was dying.

Author's note:

At the time of writing, the problem of toxic dust is still going on in the northern region of Thailand, and yet no one is paying as much attention to it anymore, simply because it's not happening in the capital. Countries like South Korea and China are also suffering from a similar situation with toxic dust pollution.

LIBERTY MOUNTAIN

Killing Stars

Hanan Adi, 15

UNITED ARAB EMIRATES AND GERMANY

ONCE UPON A TIME, there were stars.

Fields of stars. Realms of them. Galaxies. Worlds—and we could see them.

Once upon a time, the stars we saw were not merely the delight of the eye, the wonder to the heart, or the proof of the existence of God. When the day's compass retired below the hazy horizon, and all was cold and dark, the stars marked the ways. The stars were the hope.

There are no stars now. The fumes have enshrouded them. The fumes from those belching fossil-fuel power plants that have been belching for decades now, and, as long as it's profitable for the government, that will obligingly belch for the decades to come.

As we zoom past those smokestacks, belching assiduously, incessantly, I am repulsed. Then I wonder.

Do they not realize, those businessmen in their palaces and mansions, what it means to lose the stars? The bejeweled field of heaven is the smallest, yet the greatest, thing they could ever lose. Small, for it is so far away and of no market value. Great, for it is the ancient promise of health and comfort—of life itself—further along the right path.

But the big men don't care for ancient anymore—it's all the newest innovation, the newest technology, this advancement here and this development there. What held us together no longer matters; what holds us now is a complex net of business transactions and convenience.

"We," according to the big men, "we do not interact commercially with posterity. So what if our great-grandchildren breathe in polluted air? So what if fifty years hence, every other young child contracts asthma and every other venerable elder buckles under lung cancer? We live in and answer for the present only; let their respective generations attend to the past and the future.

I expect it is easy to forget; comfort and contentment are anesthetics to worry. The window is open as the jeep courses down the highway, and my hair like a banner behind me sails. Though the smokestacks have not passed from sight, the cool rushing wind is anything but unrefreshing. For a long instant, I ignore that I ride in a machine that coughs copious carbon, a mobile smokestack itself, and let the speed invigorate me.

The sun and the crescent sink; we are racing to meet them at the rim of the earth. We are almost there.

We are thirty miles and more from any civilization. Nothing has changed, perhaps for centuries. Westward stretches dune upon dune beyond dune like golden waves frozen in time. The sunset crowns each breaker with fiery foam that blinds the eye.

Shouldering the disassembled tent, the water, the telescope, and all paraphernalia that we did not believe we could stand a night without, we sink our feet in the chilly sand, tread the ancient way.

The tent is mounted and campfire lit. I watch the smoke billow and curl, higher and higher, till it merges with the darkness of the evening above. I wonder if the elders who cleave to those old, old ways instar the sky nightly with their tears; I wonder how long until even those remote haunts of theirs are choked with the carbon fumes. Then those tears all shall fall—caustic, undrinkable—and posterity will weep in its turn; but now, what do those profiteers care?

My father has mounted the telescope. By now, the crescent has slipped beneath sight, and my eyes are wide, straining, seeking.

Weeping.

"What's the matter?" He leaves the telescope, seeing the shine in my eyes.

"Look," I whisper, and point.

The North Star.

"What about it?"

"I—I can see it."

"I know, right? You can see it better through the lens. Hold on, let me focus it."

I don't need a lens. That single naked star is the most beautiful and fateful thing of all the carbon-choked earth. Polaris always led the stars, the hope.

I reach a hand forward, as though my fingers, so small suddenly against the background of the endless heavens, could seize the hope, preserve it, in their feeble grasp. But, reconsidering, I lower my hand. One by one, the celestial lamplighter is kindling them: the other stars blink and shimmer forth, some bashfully and some boldly, all beautifully.

Leave the North Star to posterity—they will well need it who follow us. There remains hope for us yet.

But how long will that hope last? The cold night is long, and though I am loath to wrench my gaze from the sky, I fall, anyhow, to sleep. Just at twilight I rise, where one by one the lamplighter extinguishes the bright little dots. How swiftly they are put out!—Stay, stay!

They each are smothered, one by one.

Those who wallow in the luxury of profit, if they would but spend one night as once did their forebears, stripped of their mansions, silks and silvers, BMWs and private jets—then they would see. There is no such thing as past, present, or future: it is but one continuum of time that the heavens lead to eternity. The hope of the past is the hope of the present and the hope of the future—but they are killing that hope, disappointing the past, bereaving the future. The sun is brimming yonder, and the businessmen believe they rise to the auspices of a new day.

Yet there are no auspices. The stars are fading.

Biographies

THOUGH THE AUTHORS included in this volume penned their pieces as members of the Write the World community while in high school, many have now ventured on to new and exciting journeys. We invite you to read about these young writers (and our two talented young illustrators) below.

HANAN ADI

Now a medical student, Hanan is originally from Canada. Her writing is deeply influenced by her love of nature and language.

AKHILA BANDLORA

Akhila Bandlora, a high school senior in Phoenix, is the cofounder and copresident of Creative Youth of Arizona. A recipient of Bow Seat's 2017 Gold Award for poetry, she believes that art is one of the most effective ways young people can get involved in their community and stimulate discussions.

ALIYAH BANERJEE

Aliyah is primarily interested in writing short stories and poetry. After publishing a poetry compilation in January 2017, she currently is a fact checker for MediaWise and an ambassador for The Cramm. Born in Delhi, India, she is also a passionate Kathak dancer. Aliyah now lives in Austin, Texas.

EMMA BARRY

Emma is a passionate young artist from Australia. She loves to draw animals. Her love for animals also fuels her care for the environment and involvement with learning about climate change.

NORAH BRADY

Norah Brady is a hypothetical astronaut, an ekphrastic poet, and a haunted house. Her poetry and short fiction works can be found in *Rookie* magazine, the *Blue Marble Review*, and the *Ekphrastic Review*. Her work has also been recognized by the Scholastic Art and Writing Awards.

SOPHIA BLOOM

Sophia Bloom is an aspiring novelist from Florida. Now in college, she is pursuing a degree in creative writing and wrote "For Florida" while in the 11th grade.

OLIVIA CAMPOS

Olivia Campos is a senior from Long Beach, California. When she isn't writing, she's painting portraits, baking, and nerding-out about the periodic table.

RAIN CASTAÑEDA

Rain is currently a computer science student at the University of the Philippines. Her passion for journalistic writing and technology drives her to use digital platforms to share information and raise awareness on societal issues that are relevant to her fellow teenagers.

BENJAMIN CHIPMAN

Benjamin Chipman is a freshman at Duke University in North Carolina, studying Environmental Science and Policy and International

Comparative Studies. As a PADI Divemaster, his love for the ocean has manifested itself in his written and verbal environmental advocacy. He hopes to continue writing and raising awareness for environmental issues.

VANI DADOO

Vani has a passion for writing about the things she sees around her in life, especially the cultural cities of Delhi and Mumbai, India. She also likes to feed her soul with bits of poetry and by watching the rain when not studying science.

PRAMIT DAS

Pramit is a 16-year-old student living in New Delhi, India. He likes cars, playing the guitar, and learning about new cultures. His long-term goals include being happy and owning a Mazda RX7.

KASEY DELBEN

Kasey is a high school student in Far North Queensland, Australia. She loves team sports, music, and fiction novels but is an expert in deliberation, procrastination, and indecision when it comes to her own work. Kasey often finds writing inspiration among the green hills and clear skies of her hometown.

GRACE FITZPATRICK

Grace is a senior in high school living in Santa Barbara, California. She enjoys playing tennis, reading, and creating art.

KATE GARDNER

Kate began writing at 12 years old after entering a youth poetry group. Her writing draws on nature, particularly the ocean, and a long-standing fascination with classic myth.

ASTRIAN HORSBURGH

Astrian is most likely to be found drinking coffee, on public transit, or in a garden, or yelling about politics somewhere. She was raised in Massachusetts and is now in college in California, studying geography.

SIRIN JITKLONGSUB

Sirin is 17 years old and is from Bangkok, Thailand. She loves writing short stories, poems, essays, and pretty much everything except autobiographies.

AINSLEY KENNEDY

Ainsley is a shy writer from the Midwestern United States who spends most of her time either thinking about her characters or penning novels. You'll likely find her in a coffee shop, listening to music and drinking hot chocolate as she attempts to finish her NaNoWriMo novel.

SHANTI MATHIAS

Shanti is a student and journalist who lives in New Zealand. She likes going for long runs, talking too much, and spending time in forests.

LINDSEY MAURER

Lindsey is a high school student from Ohio who writes the occasional poem in her spare time. She spends most of her time on Science Olympiad.

MAI MCGAW

Mai is a transgender maker from the rain-drenched Northwestern United States who enjoys walks in the woods and collecting the shiny broken things the world leaves behind. Mai intends to dedicate their life to fighting for radical change and justice for those who have been disenfranchised by systemic oppression.

LEI MESINA

Originally from the Philippines, Lei now lives in Japan. She loves how simple words strung precisely together can create worlds and spark emotions. She has constantly battled her mom for their cat's love and affection but is sadly defeated every time. She is an avid lover of rice and winter.

MICO ALDMAR TUIZA MENDOZA

Mico Mendoza is a young wordsmith from a small town in the province of Tarlac, Philippines. He finds writing to be a transformative mode of self-expression and limitless creativity. He likes speculative fiction, alternative folk music, blue-eyed kittens, and good, comfy chairs.

NIDA MIR

Nida Mir is a 16-year-old Pakistani student whose essence lies in expression, color, and hope. She animates and moulds her vivid thoughts through words. She reads inscriptions that make scenarios dance within her eyes. She bakes and devours her sugary creations. She dwells amongst smiles; she lets faith fuel her aspirations.

LIBERTY MOUNTAIN

Liberty lives in Scotland and has had a passion for art as long as she can remember. Having lived all around the world, she is excited to use her artwork to illustrate these inspiring stories about our wonderful planet.

JYOTSNA NAIR

Jyotsna Nair is a 16-year-old currently living in India who loves making things up and writing them down later. She is passionate about reading a lot, debating even more, and baking banana bread in between.

KIMBERLEY PANG

Kimberley is a 17-year-old aspiring writer from Singapore. Amidst the rigour of life as a junior college student, her imagination never fails to take her outside the boundaries of the classroom, and she continues to explore her love for writing.

GAYATRI RAJAN

Impassioned writer by day and voracious reader by night, Gayatri Rajan adores the heart-stopping, blood-racing, spine-tingling craft of writing. A high school student in Massachusetts, she has been recognized by *Imagine* magazine, the National Council of Teachers of English, Creative Kids, Write the World, and the Alliance for Young Artists & Writers. In addition to writing, she enjoys playing violin, dancing, painting, crocheting, and computer programming.

EMILY RICE

Emily Rice is a 19-year-old undergraduate at Oregon State University. She is working towards a bachelor's degree in climate science and wants to study potential solutions to global warming. She was 16 when she wrote the short story "Peepers," and she is still just as passionate about writing and environmental issues. Her dream is for humans to work together to create a habitable planet for future generations.

GEN RYAN

Gen lives in suburban Australia, and all year round (but particularly to escape the summer heat) she loves to write. She enjoys reading romantic poetry and has aimed to improve her work within this genre over her five years with Write the World and in her school's writer's club.

EVA TERRY

Despite her love for creative writing, Eva wants to be a maths teacher, oddly enough. Eva is from the UK and she is most likely to be found poring over a maths or physics problem, baking, or reading a book. Right now, she is very excited by *Great British Bake Off* and *Strictly Come Dancing* being back on TV.

ELISA TRONCOSO-CABELLO

Elisa Troncoso-Cabello is a Chilean-American writer and visual artist based in Greensboro, North Carolina. Her writing involves themes of religion, sexuality, and cultural identity, and she's lived in many different countries. She's currently in ninth grade and hopes to study art or writing in Paris or New York City.

TESSY WAUGH

With a love of nature, Tessy can often be found outdoors, whether it's mountain biking or stalking Canada's beautiful wildlife with her camera. She is an enthusiastic crafter and has an unhealthy obsession with/knowledge of Greek Mythology.

Reader's Guide

DEAR READERS (AND WRITERS),

The following questions are designed as entry points into the ideas and themes explored in this collection. We hope they will prompt your own reflections, writing, and responses. As you peruse the pieces, we encourage you to keep a journal or notebook on hand. Allow the voices collected here to inspire your own voice on the page. We are all Writers on Earth.

1. The contributors to this book are young writers from 13 countries, crisscrossing the globe from Canada to Pakistan, the United Kingdom to Thailand, the United States to the Philippines. How does the global nature of the collection change your reading experience? What impact does the geographical diversity of these voices have on you?

2. The first section of this book is made up of reflections. Somewhere in-between essay, story, and poetry, the reflection genre offers a unique perspective on the human experience. Read through three to five reflections, and then see if you can answer these questions for yourself: What is a reflection? What makes a reflection a powerful literary tool and a memorable reading experience?

3. Pieces like "Peepers," "Roots," and "Killing Stars" describe intergenerational connection and intergenerational change.

How do these pieces give you pause about your own lived experience? In what way is your environmental reality different from that of your parents' and grandparents'? In what way is it similar?

4. Pieces like "Kingfisher" and "Winter Sunrise" capture the essence of wonder. Write your own poem or short reflection about your own moment of wonder in the natural world.

5. "Dynamics, Predators, Islands" and "This Quiet Northern Wild" offer perspectives on paradox. What points are these writers trying to make, and how does the tool of paradox help them make it?

6. "Never Forget" is written as a three-part poem. What impact does this structure have on the reading experience? Why do you think the writer chose to divide her stanzas into these three distinct parts? If you were to utilize this structure in a poem of your own, what subject matter do you think would lend itself to this style?

7. Rachel Carson is best known for her groundbreaking reporting on the pesticide DDT. But long before Carson wrote *Silent Spring* in 1962, she was viewing the world as an artist and a naturalist, and writing down her observations in vignettes that would eventually be collected, published, and celebrated. In these writings, Carson seemed to slow down time, allowing us to notice details about water, shadows, birds, waves. Some of the remarkable pieces in this collection offer the same gift to readers. Notice how, in a piece like "Kingfisher," the writer highlights things about his subject that only come from close observation. Now, it's your turn to become a witness. Wherever you are in the world, take a close observation of something in

nature, and then turn your observation into art: write, draw, take a photo, or create a song.

8. Pieces like "The Forest . . . No, Stadium, in My Backyard" and "Drought" contend with environmental changes in the writers' lives. Depending on what corner of the globe we call home, the world around us can change in many different ways. What changes have you witnessed in your lifetime, in the place you call home?

9. In this age of climate crisis, it can be challenging to find sources of solace and hope. Nonetheless, many of the pieces in this collection offer just that. Which pieces did you find most hopeful? Why?

10. "One for the Basket, One for Me" and "Into the World" invite the reader into a particular place through a sensory experience. Notice how the writers use some or all of the five senses to bring their worlds to life, and then write your own sensory-rich description.

11. Zoomorphism is a literary device in which the writer takes on the point of view of an animal, such as the piece "Seagull" in this collection. How did this change the reading experience for you? Try writing your own poem or vignette from the perspective of an animal.

12. "Untamed Beauty," "Anthropocene Echoes," and "Ariel's Gallery" offer perspectives on self and identity. How are these pieces different and how are they similar? What phrases do you find most effective in each?

13. Haikus are traditionally focused on an aspect of the natural world. Read the haiku in this collection—"Give Me Back My

Winter"—and then write your own, taking note of the three-line structure and the 5/7/5 syllable count.

14. "Metaphoric Trees" is a beautiful slip of a poem that uses metaphor to cast trees in a new light, while "We Ran as if to Meet the Moon" does the same with the moon as its subject. Notice how the metaphors compare trees and the moon to something (an object, a feeling, a place, a sound) to which they are not literally applicable in order to give the reader a richer understanding of their essence. Now it's your turn! Write your own tree or moon metaphor, finding a fresh way to describe these wonders.

15. "Creeper in a Crack" captures the beauty of entropy (disorder/deterioration). Read the poem again, taking note of the details the writer uses to beckon the reader into this place, and then write your own poem about the intersection of the human world and the natural world.

16. Many of the pieces in the "Narrative" section of the book weave together personal experiences with political or social opinions and/or observations. Which piece did you find most successful in striking this balance? What about it worked well for you, as the reader?

17. Pieces like "Stranded," "Saving Ourselves from Ourselves," and "Sound the Silent Alarm" wield a certain power when written by authors in their youth. What is it about the young writers' voices in these pieces that lend so much authority to the topic?

Acknowledgments

WE ACKNOWLEDGE Rosabeth Moss Kanter, Ernest L. Arbuckle Professor of Business Administration at Harvard Business School; Fernando M. Reimers, Professor of International Education at Harvard Graduate School of Education; and Nancy Sommers, Lecturer at Harvard Graduate School of Education, for their ongoing support and inspiration. We thank Maureen Forys, Jeff Lytle, and everyone at Happenstance Type-O-Rama, and Jason Grant and Jordan McGuire at Inkahoots for transforming our manuscript into a beautiful book. We are grateful for the support of our partners for our Earth Day Writing Competition, including Earth Day Network, Children's Environmental Literacy Foundation, and Bow Seat Ocean Awareness. We recognize our talented young illustrators, Liberty Mountain and Emma Barry, who created the artwork throughout the publication. And finally, a big thank you to our young writers, their teachers, guardians, parents, and friends who made this publication possible.